DISNEY'S
The Fox and the Hound
Hide-and-Seek

Tod was a lively young fox who lived on a farm. His friend Copper was a long-eared, big-footed hound pup who lived down the road. Tod and Copper did everything together.

They swam
in the pond.

They chased chickens
out of the barn.

They helped Boomer the woodpecker and
Dinky the sparrow hunt for caterpillars.
Sometimes they just sat
under the oak tree and talked
with Big Mama the owl.

Every day as Tod watched Copper go
home, he felt a sad, empty feeling inside.
'Honey,' said Big Mama, 'that empty
feeling is called being lonely.'

One afternoon when Copper came to play,
Tod was tired of chasing chickens and looking
for caterpillars and staying around the farm.

'Let's go exploring in the forest!' he said eagerly.

'That sounds like fun,' Copper said. 'I'll race
you across the meadow.'

'You two ought to wait till tomorrow morning,' Big Mama called after them. 'It gets dark quickly in the forest – you might get lost.'

'Don't worry,' Tod said. 'We'll be careful.' And off they ran.

It was cool and dim in the forest. The trees were close together and their leafy branches shut out the sky. The only sounds were the chirping of birds and the rustling of small animals in the undergrowth.

'What a good place for hide-and-seek!' cried Tod. 'Want to play, Copper? I'll hide, and you look for me.'

'Okay,' said Copper.
'I'll find you, too.'
Copper covered his
eyes and started counting
while Tod looked for
a place to hide.

'If I stay close by, he's sure to find me,' Tod
thought. So he ran past trees and mossy rocks and
swam across a little stream. Then he ran some
more. Finally, he stopped at a hollow tree stump.
'This is the perfect place,' he thought. 'Copper
will never find me here!'

He crawled into the stump and curled
up. It was cozy and warm and Tod was tired
from all the running he'd done. Before he
knew it, he was fast asleep.

Meanwhile, Copper had finished counting and was looking for Tod. He put his nose to the ground, as hound dogs do, and sniffed for Tod's scent.

He sniffed at a clump of tall grass. There was a beating of wings and a quail flew out.

He sniffed at some
dry leaves under
a big beech tree.
Two squirrels jumped
out and ran up the tree.

He sniffed around a fallen log and a prickly porcupine rattled its quills at him.

At last, Copper picked up Tod's scent. He followed it to the stream and he swam across. But when he got to the other side and started sniffing again, there was no trace of Tod.

Copper began to get worried. 'What if it gets dark before I find Tod?' he thought.

It *was* dark when Tod woke up.

'Copper didn't find me', he thought as he climbed out of the tree stump. 'Maybe he went home without me. I'll never be able to find my way home by myself.'

Tod was frightened.

Suddenly, he heard something move behind him. He turned around. Two eyes gleamed in the darkness. 'It must be a bear,' Tod thought, trembling. 'Oh, I wish Copper were here!' He was so scared that he began to cry.

'Tod, is that you?' a shaky little voice asked.
'Copper!' Tod exclaimed. 'You found me!
I thought you were a bear.'

'I'm so glad I found you,' Copper said. 'I was frightened all by myself in the dark.'

'So was I,' Tod said. 'I thought you had gone home and left me here alone.'

'I wouldn't do that,' said Copper. 'We're friends. Friends stick together and help each other out.'

Tod and Copper huddled close to each other to keep warm. 'It's not so scary in the forest when you have a friend to keep you company,' Tod said.

'Everything's easier when you have a friend,' said Copper. 'Tomorrow morning, we'll help each other find the way home.'

'No need to wait that long,'
said a voice above them. It was
Big Mama.

'I had a feeling you two might need
some help,' she said. 'When you weren't
back by sunset, I figured I'd better
come looking for you.'

'We're glad you did, Big Mama,' Copper said.
'Thank you.'

'Well, honey, you're my friends,' said Big Mama.
'Friends take care of each other. Now, you just
follow me and I'll have you home in no time.'

When they were out of the forest and
across the meadow, Tod and Copper started
to say goodbye.

'Copper, will we always be friends?' Tod asked.

'Forever and ever,' said Copper. 'Maybe even
longer than that.'

The little hound started
down the road to his home.
This time, Tod didn't feel a bit
lonely as he watched Copper
go. He knew that no matter
how often Copper left, he'd
always come back. After all,
he was a friend, and that's
what friends do.

Treasure Cove Stories

1 Three Little Pigs
2 Snow White
& The Seven Dwarfs
3 The Fox and the Hound
- Hide and Seek
4 Dumbo
5 Cinderella
6 Cinderella's Friends
7 Alice In Wonderland
8 Mad Hatter's Tea Party
from Alice In Wonderland
9 Mickey Mouse and
his Spaceship
10 Peter Pan
11 Pinocchio
12 Mickey Mouse Flies
the Christmas Mail
13 Sleeping Beauty
and the Good Fairies
14 The Lucky Puppy
15 Chicken Little
16 Mother Goose
17 Coco
18 Winnie-the-Pooh and Tigger
19 The Sword in the Stone
20 Mary Poppins
21 The Jungle Book
22 Aristocats
23 Lady and the Tramp
24 Bambi
25 Bambi - Friends
of the Forest
26 Pete's Dragon
27 Beauty & The Beast
- The Teapot's Tale
28 Monsters, Inc.
- M is for Monster
29 Finding Nemo
30 The Incredibles
31 The Incredibles
- Jack-Jack Attack
32 Ratatouille
- Your Friend the Rat
33 Wall-E
34 Up
35 Princess and the Frog

36 Toy Story - The Pet Problem
37 Dora the Explorer - Dora and
the Unicorn King
38 Dora the Explorer
- Grandma's House
39 Spider-Man
- Night of the Vulture!
40 Wreck-it Ralph
41 Brave
42 The Invincible Iron Man
- Eye of the Dragon
43 SpongeBob SquarePants
- Sponge in Space!
44 SpongeBob SquarePants
- Where the Pirates Arrrgh!
45 Toy Story - A Roaring
Adventure
46 Cars - Deputy Mater
Saves the Day!
47 Spider-Man
- Trapped By The Green Goblin
48 Big Hero 6
49 Spider-Man - High Voltage!
50 Frozen
51 Cinderella Is My Babysitter
52 Beauty & The Beast
- I Am The Beast
53 Blaze and the Monster
Machines - Mighty Monster
Machines
54 Blaze and the Monster
Machines - Dino Parade!
55 Teenage Mutant Ninja Turtles
- Follow The Ninja!
56 I Am A Princess
57 Paw Patrol
- The Big Book of Paw Patrol
58 Paw Patrol
- Adventures with Grandpa
59 Merida Is My Babysitter
60 Trolls
61 Trolls Holiday Special
62 The Secret Life of Pets
63 Zootropolis
64 Ariel Is My Babysitter
65 Inside Out

66 Belle Is My Babysitter
67 The Lion Guard
- Eye In The Sky
68 Moana
69 Finding Dory
70 Guardians of the Galaxy
71 Captain America
- High-Stakes Heist!
72 Ant-Man
73 The Mighty Avengers
74 The Mighty Avengers
- Lights Out!
75 The Incredible Hulk
76 Shimmer & Shine
- Wish upon a Sleepover
77 Shimmer & Shine
- Backyard Ballet
78 Paw Patrol - All-Star Pups!
79 Teenage Mutant Ninja Turtles
- Really Spaced Out!
80 Cars 2 - Travel Buddies
81 Madagascar
82 Jasmine Is My Babysitter
83 How To Train Your Dragon
84 Shrek
85 Puss In Boots
86 Kung Fu Panda
87 Beauty & The Beast
- I Am Belle
88 The Lion Guard
- The Imaginary Okapi
89 Thor - Thunder Strike
90 Guardians of the Galaxy
-Rocket to the Rescue
91 Nella The Princess Knight
- Nella and the Dragon
92 Shimmer & Shine
- Treasure Twins!
93 Olaf's Frozen Adventure
94 Black Panther
95 Branch's Bunker Birthday
96 Shimmer & Shine
- Pet Talent Show

Book list may be subject to change.

An ongoing series to collect and enjoy!